The Scooter Race

By Jackie Tidey

Illustrations by Lyn Stone

Contents

At Dad's House

On Sunday,
I went to my dad's house for the day.
I took my **scooter** with me
because I wanted to race Ben and Nick.
They live next door to Dad.

A Scooter Race

After lunch,
we had races on our scooters
along the path, outside the houses.
Dad watched us having fun.

Then Dad said he would take us
to Greenway Park.
We would have a much better race
down there.

At Greenway Park

Lots of big girls and boys
were on the scooter **ramps**,
when we got to the park.
They were showing off and doing tricks.

Joe Brown was there, too.
He is the Scooter Champ at this park.
He did a big jump over some bars.

Then he came over to talk to us.
All the children at the park like Joe.

A Place to Race

Dad found us a good place
to have our race.
It was on a big path.

He said we would have to race
down that path, around some trees
to a flower garden, and back again.

The first **rider** to get back to the start line
would win the race.

The Race Starts

Ben, Nick and I waited behind the line.
We were ready for Dad
to start the race.

Dad waved a flag
and we raced off like rockets.

The Half-Way Mark

Ben, Nick and I went as fast as we could along the path.

I got to the flower garden just before Ben.
As we turned our scooters around
to race back,
Nick came flying along past the last tree.

The Race Ends

Ben raced past me on the way back.
I tried to catch him,
but he was too fast for me.

Ben was the winner!

Joe Brown and some of the big boys
had come over to watch our race.

We had a great time with Dad on Sunday.

Glossary

ramps   places for riding scooters

rider   someone who rides a scooter

scooter   a toy with wheels and handle bars